Workbook

for

Outlive

An Essential guide to Peter Attia's Book

The Science and Art of Longevity

Genie Reads

Table of Contents

How To Use This Workbook

Hello there!

It is with great pleasure to see that you have taken an interest in the book "Outlive" by Peter Attia. This book by Peter highlights the importance of taking care of our health in the right way. Gone are the times when you just looked to simple medicine for your sickness and hoped that your life can be as long and disease-free as possible. These days, Peter shows us how we are able to effectively prevent and safeguard ourselves from many chronic ailments which plague the population. Using his approach, you will be tackling the issue of how to live longer, and be meaningfully healthy and active with that longevity.

This workbook is meant to enhance and highlight the ideas and concepts mentioned, so that it makes it very much easier for you to take action and implement what you have learnt from the book into practical, daily usage. With the aid of this workbook, making efforts to improve your longevity becomes much easier through the step-by-step guidance and systematic approaches highlighted within. Equipped with the knowledge and practical skillsets developed through the workbook's exercises, you can be sure that you will be able to garner a much deeper understanding of the methodologies recommended by Dr Attia as well as bring forth positive change in your life and the lives of those around you. In order to absorb quicker and with a lasting impact, it is vital that you answer all the questions presented in the workbook, and answer them sincerely. Only by digging deep and giving honest answers will you be able to flash light on what truly matters to you, and get the opportunities to effect lasting positive change in your daily life.

The workbook will also feature important summaries of each individual chapter, which will be integral in helping you answer the questions contained therein. As such, for the time constrained folk, you do not necessarily need to read the main book before answering the questions in this workbook. All the crucial points have been condensed and captured for your attention. For the folks whom have already read the book, the afore mentioned salient concepts will serve well as quick reminders and gentle nudges when you are doing the questions.

Whilst attempting the questions found in the workbook, please take your time to go through it carefully. This portion is an area where speedy reading can be set aside and replaced with thoughtful ruminations. The questions will encourage you to reflect and think, sometimes very deeply, before you jump in with any answers. It will be of great benefit to you if the answers supplied are colored with the honesty of thought and tinged with sincerity. After all, no one can be as interested in your welfare as your own self.

Done in this careful, constructive way, you will be able to harness the positive change created and see it reverberate throughout many aspects of your life. For some, the honest answers may create self criticism. Take heart, know that you are not alone, and that by just the mere act of acknowledgement of mistakes made in the past, that itself is a very important step forward.

You will want to come back to these questions again after your initial foray, say after a period of 4 to 8 weeks; there really is no set in stone time length, but it is highly recommended to have at least a space of 4 weeks between the first and second attempt at the questions. This second try is really to let you see the progress you have made, both in thoughts and actions, and also to think of different angles to the same questions with your new life experiences.

You can really repeat this process as many times as you find useful. The key is always honesty in the answers and an indefatigable spirit for self development and progress.

May you be well and be happy.

Introduction

Dr. Peter Attia trained to become a doctor specializing in cancer. It's a demanding job, not just because it takes years of study and the need for working close to perfection before you can become one but also because of the constant dealings with loss and emotional pain.

Peter had to deal with death almost every day of his life. He had to look mortality in the eye. More often than not, Peter felt helpless about his situation. He knew he couldn't save everyone but still, he would like to keep trying.

However, he changed careers when he realized the futility of scrambling to save all his patients. This time, he is working toward preventing what he would call Horsemen diseases from happening.

One night, he had a dream reflecting on what was happening in his life. He found himself trying to catch eggs being thrown down from a rooftop. He wasn't exactly sure why the person doing the throwing was doing it, but he tried his best to catch all the eggs.

Of course, he wasn't able to. That helplessness led to the realization that what he should be doing was preventing the guy from throwing the eggs down at all. He has to go to the source of the problem.

Most of our night dreams get lost in a haze when we wake up. However, this particular dream remained with Dr. Attia. It still resonates with him because it represents his role in life.

Attia changed his career so that he could address the cancer problem. As a young surgeon, he knew that he wouldn't be able to save everyone. That realization came early when Peter witnessed his first death. The ones he had treated and went into remission might still die not too long after the treatment.

Knowing his limitations had set Attia on a mission – to promote longevity. It's why his book Outlive: The Science and Art of Longevity was written.

This workbook provides the concise, important details and it provides a quick summary of the lessons he taught while allowing you to be more proactive in using the knowledge.

Here, you will find the crucial condensation and insightful delivery of Dr. Peter Attia's words as well as a guide that you can use to apply what you have learned in your life. Don't just learn about longevity. Strive towards a healthy, productive life span.

PART ONE

Ch 1: The Long Game from Fast Death to Slow Death

Summary

Peter explains his relationship with death. He was badly shaken by a death he witnessed in his second year as a doctor. It was the first definite sign that he couldn't save everyone.

Seeing a patient die right before his eyes awakened a curiosity about longevity. How long do people live? Can people live a good life for longer?

The thing is, longevity isn't even just about how long a person lives. He realizes that some people live higher quality lives. In contrast, others may live longer than expected but struggle through life.

So, he thought of the concepts of fast death and slow death. There was a time when people died fast deaths. Nowadays, though, you'd hear more about slow deaths. These deaths don't happen right away. It takes some time for someone to die of cancer, diabetes, and many other chronic diseases. It's not the longevity people should be aiming for.

Time has managed to give scientists a chance to find cures for cardiovascular diseases. It has helped them extend the life of people suffering from these conditions. However, extending life can have its pros and cons if the person is sick. Instead of having a long life, it feels like people are moving towards a slow death.

More often than not, people who die from chronic diseases have tackled the issue too late. You've probably heard of people getting checked and finding out they are already at a later stage of cancer. Notably, Peter refers to chronic diseases that cause slow death as ""Horsemen"" diseases.

Lessons

1. Longevity is more complicated than it may first seem nowadays.

2. Longevity is not just living long but living a high-quality life longer.

3. Slow death is becoming more common than fast death.

4. It would help if you cared for both your physical and mental health.

Issues Surrounding the Subject Matter

1. Do you find the subject of mortality frightening?

2. Are there people in your family who died at a young age?

3. What about family members who died slowly from severe illness?

4. So far, what is the quality of your health and life?

Goals

1. Live life with good health in mind.

2. Understand the term longevity.

3. Aim for true longevity.

4. Learn to make healthy choices.

Action Steps

1. Prepare your mindset to make sure you keep yourself healthy.

2. Choose healthy every time you have a choice between habits and practices.

3. Think freely about how you would want to maintain a good quality of life for long term instead of just heading for a slow death. To do this, it would be good for you to

scribble in the box provided below, or you can do it on a blank piece of paper.

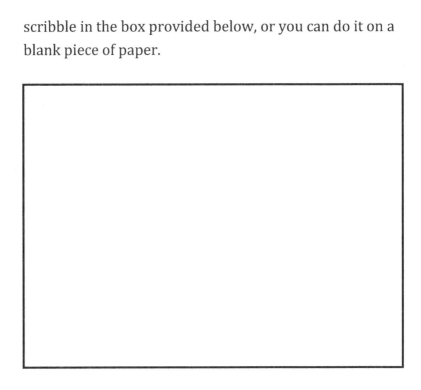

After you have done so, look through your thoughts that you have scribbled while free associating and seek to find linkages between them. This exercise is to help you find any possible points which maybe be residing in your sub conscious and help flesh it out for your reference.

4. Start a health journal to record the following:
   a. Family History
   b. Current Medical Conditions
   c. Medications Taken

Checklist

1. Go to your annual physical.

2. Get regularly checked by your doctor, especially if you have a chronic health condition or your family has a high risk of some of the so-called Horsemen diseases.

3. Eat healthy foods. Get some advice from a nutritionist if needed.

4. Give some time for regular exercise. If you have any muscle or bone issues or are a little older, you may want to consult a doctor before you proceed with a regimen.

5. Sleep for the prescribed hours specific to your age.

Ch 2: Medicine 3.0: Rethinking Medicine for the Age of Chronic Disease

Summary

In this chapter, Peter describes three stages of medical history, Medicine 1.0, 2.0, and 3.0.

Medicine 1.0 refers to the time centuries ago when people went through ""guesswork"" treatments. The folks had to go through all sorts of procedures that might or might not work. The age expectancy was also very short.

Medicine 2.0 refers to the mid-nineteenth century when people began understanding the need for lab testing and better sanitation. It was at this time that penicillin was invented. It was a time of breakthrough, with smallpox, polio, and other deadly diseases finally being dealt with.

As medicine improved, more diseases also came to fore. It's why there's a need for a stage called Medicine 3.0.

Medicine 3.0 is made up of four critical parts or points:

- The emphasis on prevention over cure (although it doesn't mean that the search for cures has slowed down
- The individuality of people – recognizing the fact that one treatment may not fit everyone.
- A look at people's attitudes to risks – some people seem more prone to taking risks with their health than others
- People are moving towards a better, healthy life

Even though Medicine 2.0 had seen a surge in medical developments, that period still couldn't do much to help sick people. Peter asks us to focus on Medicine 3.0 because it is the era that brought so many technological advancements. Due to the fact that illnesses have somehow evolved into more potent threats, there is a need to raise the bar regarding medicine.

Medicine 3.0 does not look at one solution. It considers the individuality of the person we are focusing on and tailors answers for that individual.

Lessons

1. Throughout the centuries, humans have tried their best to find ways to live longer.

2. Medical advancements improve the way people live.

3. Medicine 3.0 is the most promising era for people with Horsemen diseases.

4. Medicine 3.0 has a lot to do with the improved longevity of people.

5. Each person needs a unique approach to becoming healthier.

Issues Surrounding the Subject Matter

1. What are some of today's technologies and medications that have specifically improved your life or the life of someone you know?

2. Do you know someone in your life who could have benefited from Medicine 3.0 treatments and approaches if they had lived during this time?

Goals

1. Apply the knowledge of Medicine 3.0 to your lifestyle

2. Understand the importance of counteracting risks with better healthcare

3. Regularly get checked so that technology can help prevent diseases, or at least detect them early so that Medicine 3.0 can effectively help eradicate them

Action Steps

1. Be aware of the latest technologies in medicine

2. Ask your doctor about treatments for any possible illnesses you or a family member may have

3. Add another section to your health journal: medication and technological advancements that may have saved the life of someone you know (e.g., MRI)

Checklist

1. Get regularly checked by your doctor, especially if you're at high risk of developing Horsemen diseases (have a family with cardiovascular diseases, diabetes, or cancer)

2. Self-examine for worrisome situations that need checking (e.g., lumps for breast cancer)

3. Do not wholly avoid risks but understand how you can deal with them

4. Use all the medical technologies and advantages to help you live a longer, healthier life

5. In order to know how to effectively prevent the diseases which you might be at risk of, you will need to pick up

on knowledge in order to do just that. Take a thorough look at your body and note any areas which you might be having potential issues. Proceed with the in-depth body scans and tests by your doctor during your annual physical. After which will be your job to soak up any information on the conditions which you might have, and learn how to deal with them effectively. One important thing is do not just keep your knowledge field to that of traditional medicine, do take note of holistic or other forms of healing as well.

Ch 3: Objective Strategy Tactics: A Road Map for Reading this Book

Summary

In this chapter, Peter discusses the three-part approach to aiming for longevity. The three parts include objective, strategy, and tactics.

He refers to the final decades of our life as the Marginal Decade. It is when we should be well aware of our life span and be clear about what we want to happen during those years.

On the opposite side of the Marginal Decade is the Bonus Decade. Not only are you looking at what the final years will be like, but you're also finding ways to improve your longevity. It would be best if you were working on adding a bonus decade to your life.

But before you try to understand everything all at once, let's return to the three parts: objective, strategy, and tactics.

Well, the objective gets clearer in every chapter. We're supposed to look at our lives and see how we can extend our life span, not just to add more years but to add healthy ones.

The focus is on having a high-quality life that will make the long years worth living.

Then, we look at the strategy. Peter wants us to use an evidence-supported model. This scientific model is reflective of his background in medicine and science. It's not just something that he feels should be done but something that he knows should be done.

You may think, but wait, why is he discussing a strategy followed by tactics? You may think they're the same, and I must admit I had the same thought at first, but they're actually different.

No matter how well you strategize, you will be working against time. As you age, your body deteriorates. It's a given. It's just a matter of figuring out if you can somehow slow that aging down. It's also about keeping yourself healthy for a longer period of time.

Your strategy must be used to counteract your decline in your cognitive, physical, and mental health. It is just like boxing, where one of the potential strategies used is to outlast your opponent. Outlasting the other guy would be the overarching strategy, and then from it flows the rest of your tactics.

Diseases that affect the physical and mental aspects of our being can be prevented. With our minds looking at the endgame, longevity; we should also look at some strategies we can efficiently implement into our lives.

With a good grasp of the strategies as our underlying base, we can then move on to talk about tactics.

What five tactics can we use to improve our lives and extend our life spans?

We look at **nutrition, sleep, exercise, emotional health,** and **drugs**. The first three may feel like a given. We know we have to eat well, sleep well, and get moving. However, longevity also depends on our emotional health and drugs, too. We need to apply what we know about Medicine 3.0. We should also see how crucial it is to have healthy emotional well-being.

Emotional health can affect our physical health. If we always feel down, our bodies will begin believing we aren't well. So, it is also best to take care of our mental and emotional health.

The final tactic, drugs, reminds us that we are in the Medicine 3.0 era. It's a time when we have been given enough ammunition against illnesses. We can battle slow death and live a higher quality of life with the help of some medication. We need to adjust our ways of dealing with life and health according to the times.

Lessons

1. When we plan to extend our longevity, we think of our objectives, strategies, and tactics.

2. Strategies and tactics may sound the same, but they are slightly different.

3. Our strategies should be science-based.

4. The five tactics that can help us improve our health and longevity are nutrition, sleep, exercise, caring for our emotional health, and taking necessary drugs.

Issues Surrounding the Subject Matter

1. What do you want to change or improve in your health?

2. Which of the five tactics do you have problems with?

3. Ponder on how you would go about gathering information to create your evidenced based strategies that can be used to slow aging and keep yourself healthier.

Goals

1. Create a specific game plan that will help us live longer and happier

2. Look at health in a holistic way

3. Apply both strategies and tactics that will help our health-related objectives come to fruition

Action Steps

1. Do you think you might have other objectives besides the stated one in the book about longevity? We are talking about health based objectives here, for instance, some folks may want to stay clear of pharmaceutical medicine at all costs or some others may express not want to undergo any form of surgery whatsoever. What might your own objective be?

2. Write the main points that you have gleaned from this segment regarding objectives, strategies and tactic in your health journal under Reminders

3. Identify your objectives because your subsequent actions (strategies and tactics) will depend on them

4. Create a plan using the five main tactics

Checklist

1. Create a nutritional plan according to your objective

2. File a series of exercises that will help you achieve your goal while considering your body type, age, and overall health

3. Make your bedroom comfortable for sleeping

4. Follow good sleep hygiene and a fixed ritual that will help you sleep better.

5. Find someone who you can share your worries with because you need to sound out everything that's going on inside of you.

6. Do hobbies that you enjoy or make time for entertainment

7. Get checked by a doctor regularly so that you'll know if you need to take maintenance drugs

PART TWO

Ch 4: Centenarians: The Older You Get, The Healthier You Have Been

Summary

Peter was actively curious about centenarians and whether genes greatly influence their longevity. We can't blame him. There's something about turning a hundred that inspires awe. Some governments actively recognize and reward people who reach their big 100th birthday.

According to a new England study and an experiment involving Scandinavian twins, centenarians have much to thank their genes for. This result shouldn't be much of a surprise. However, Peter wants to go further and use the benefits of such genes to help people who don't have such an advantage reach the ripe old age of one hundred.

With smart strategies and tactics and possible behavioral changes leaning more towards good health practices, we can attempt to reach a hundred, even if it's not in our genes to do so.

Studies show that though there is a more significant number of centenarian women, centenarian men show better cognitive skills at their age. Then again, only men at their peak health and condition reach the hundred-year age.

Peter discusses APOE, a potent gene that affects how we grow old. This gene carries e2, e3, and e4 variants.

APOE is responsible for cholesterol transport and processing. If you have the e4 variant, you are more susceptible to Alzheimer's. On the other hand, e2 helps prevent dementia. Meanwhile, e3 seems stuck in the middle of the two in more ways than one. It's the most common variant. It means that most of us are caught somewhere in between.

Going back to e2, having at least two types of this variant will help increase your longevity by as much as 30%. So, a lot of our life span hinges on our genes, and depends on what family we came from.

Then, there's the FOX03 gene, which sounds like it comes from a science fiction book but is real. As you may have guessed, this gene has a direct and positive impact on our longevity. Not only that, but it also helps other genes become more active and imbue our body with healthier cells.

What we can do, though, is improve our gene expression. We can use our behaviors and environment to catch up to the level that people with the advantage of genetics have.

Ultimately, we have to think about that one thing centenarians all have – resilience. Some have the full advantage of being blessed with the right genes. However, most had to back it up with good health strategies and tactics. We have to make sure that we have a set of strategies that we can use to improve your longevity.

Lessons

1. More likely than not, centenarians reach a ripe old age generally because they have the right genes.

2. Using our behaviors and environments to help us achieve the same benefits centenarians are reaping is possible.

3. The APOE gene has three variants, e3 being the most common while the other two are at the extreme ends of the spectrum, with e4 present in those who are more likely to develop Alzheimer's and e2 in those who are least likely to develop dementia.

4. Centenarian men are still more likely to have high cognitive skills. However, there is a more significant number of centenarian women.

Issues Surrounding the Subject Matter

1. What is your family life span like?

2. Do you have any centenarians in your family? If not, find out online about the more famous ones, or search around for them in your extended family or in your circle of friends. Think about their living conditions and environment when these centenarians were younger, might these conditions have aided them in any way to reach such a ripe old age?

3. Do you live in a country or city with a significant population of centenarians?

Goals

1. Practice better habits that will hopefully defeat any gene pool disadvantage.

2. Use our behavior and environment to improve our chances of reaching a hundred years old.

3. Be aware of what our bodies are capable of naturally based on our families.

Action Steps

1. Practice better health habits

2. Be more aware of what is harming your body and which is not

3. Take advantage of any good genes passed on to you

4. Create a family history based on the ages members have died. Indicate the causes of death. For example, accidents may cause someone to die young, but they wouldn't indicate the person's natural life span.

5. When the doctors and scientists talk about gene expression, how much do you know about it? This particular term may be the potential leveler between the have and have-nots of good genes. Think about how you are going to shape your environment as well as lifestyle to fully bring forward the power of gene expression. Of course, before you do that, you shall have to learn and delve into what exactly makes gene expression tick.

Checklist

1. Find out your family medical history

2. See what diseases are prevalent in your families and get checked for them

3. Practice preventative measures as advised by a doctor

4. Sometimes taking some time out for yourself may do wonders to the physical body. Perhaps you might want

to schedule in a 5 or 10 minute meditation sitting session on a daily basis, and lengthen the time span as you get more and more comfortable with sitting in unmoving silence.

Ch 5: Eat Less, Live Longer: The Science of Hunger and Health

Summary

Peter talks about the science that connects health with hunger in this chapter.

Suren Segal discovered the molecule called rapamycin, which is connected with longevity. The biochemist was the first to discover its capability to extend lifespans.

In 1999, the FDA even approved the molecule because it strengthens immune systems. It's found to be helpful to transplant patients and was found to slow down the division and growth of cells.

When amino acids drop, our bodies go through autophagy. Autophagy is essential because it puts our bodies into recycling mode, helping us eliminate trash that can eventually or is already harming our health.

Unfortunately, the body's ability to go into autophagy decreases as a person ages. However, we can try to get around this by decreasing our food intake.

The molecule rapamycin can induce autophagy. That's why it does wonders for your health to the point that it's been credited for killing cancer cells. It generally prolongs life because it keeps some diseases, like cancer, in check. It also slows down aging and many other processes that help keep one healthy and robust despite an advanced age.

Another drug that is considered to reduce or slow down aging is metformin. It's a drug that is often prescribed to people with diabetes.

Lessons

1. The molecule rapamycin can help slow down aging and keep our immune systems working as they should

2. Eating less can help your body go into autophagy

3. Rapamycin also induces autophagy

4. As one person ages, the body loses its capability to get into autophagy

5. Autophagy is an essential process in life. It helps eliminate the body's waste materials to prevent us from getting sick.

6. Rapamycin has been FDA-approved because of its benefits to the immune system.

7. Another way of slowing down aging is taking rapamycin.

Issues Surrounding the Subject Matter

1. Have you ever fasted in your life for religious or health reasons?

2. Would you be able to incorporate fasting into your life?

3. Have you decreased your food intake without affecting how you function?

Goals

1. Understand the science and importance of using rapamycin to induce autophagy.

2. Use rapamycin as we age to induce autophagy.

3. Decrease your food intake without negatively affecting your health and the way you function in your daily life.

Action Steps

1. Keep working on your general health using good health behaviors

2. Check your environment for possible toxins that may be increasing your aging process

3. Research into different fasting methodologies and see which might catch your eye

4. Look also into different types of foods which you might want to start excluding from your usual diet. Having them once in a while would be okay, but not on a daily basis

5. Record your attempts to decrease your food intake.

Food and number of calories	Previous portion	Current portion	Results of decreasing intake

Checklist

1. Get regularly checked by your physician to see if your aging is normal

2. See if rapamycin is suitable for you or if you have to wait a few more years

3. Eat less to help induce autophagy even when you're still relatively young

4. Ponder on calorie restrictive diets, where you would have to eat less throughout the day, or think about fasting, where you basically deny food to the body for certain periods of the day or week. Weigh up the pros and cons of both approaches, but most importantly see which seems to be more sustainable to you in the long term. This is crucial because you have to be able to maintain that kind of lifestyle for an extended period of time in order for it to have any beneficial effect upon yourself.

Ch 6: The Crisis of Abundance: Can Our Ancient Genes Cope with Our Modern Diet?

Summary

The previous chapter discusses how eating less can help you achieve autophagy more successfully. This chapter examines how today's modern world makes it challenging to consider eating less.

There are so many foods to choose from.

You may not think of abundance as a crisis, but it is now one. With so many varieties of food and drink on the ready, it's easy to get so caught up in feasting.

A sign that abundance is a big problem can be derived from studies which show that non-alcoholics have also been displaying signs of liver impairment. Obese people are more likely to show these signs.

Higher alanine aminotransferase (ALT) levels suggest that a person is on the way to developing liver diseases similar to those that alcoholics have. It means you don't have to ingest alcohol to damage your liver. However, even low ALT levels do not guarantee that this is not the case. You may still develop non-alcoholic fatty liver disease (NAFLD).

When NAFLD is combined with inflammation, you can experience non-alcoholic steatohepatitis (NASH).

Note that metabolic problems can cause problems like Horsemen diseases, pre-diabetes, and other health conditions. However, weight isn't always a factor. Some obese people have better metabolism than thin ones. Therefore, people of varying weights should get checked regularly.

So, how is metabolism correlated to liver diseases? Well, people with metabolic dysfunction are more likely to produce excess triglycerides. It leads to fat accumulation, insulin resistance, and NAFLD, among other harmful effects.

Dr. Attia recommends going through DEXA scanning to detect visceral fat in your body. Those with excess visceral body fat who don't exercise will have many problems. Also, you may have heard that stressed people will develop high cortisol levels. Cortisol gets rid of the good fat and packs in the visceral fat. It's not exactly what you'd want to happen.

Another component that messes with your metabolism is fructose. How? It tricks your body into thinking that you need to eat more.

These days, you have Medicine 3.0 to help you monitor any markers, such as elevated insulin, chronic inflammation, high

ALT, and more. You can correct your eating habits or take medication when needed.

Lessons

1. We still have the genes of our ancestors, the ones that are not used to abundance.

2. Obese people, people with metabolic dysfunction, and people who eat a lot for the sake of eating may develop liver problems that are often only expected in alcoholics.

3. Abundance can mess up your metabolism. Fructose and cortisol can make you pack visceral fats by tricking you into thinking you need to eat more.

4. Thankfully, there are ways to monitor the levels of chemicals in our bodies through Medicine 3.0.

5. There is good fat and bad fat. Visceral fat is terrible for your body.

6. Solid metabolic health will help you in your quest for better longevity.

Issues surrounding the subject matter

1. Do you think you gain much weight even when you eat less?

2. How many meals do you eat in a day?

3. Do you have a calorie limit?

4. Do you also snack throughout the day or during certain periods of the day? If you do snack irregularly, do you realize what usually triggers the snacking urges?

Goals

1. Understand how we get sick from eating too much

2. Ensure that we eat only the amount of food our bodies need

3. Internalize the concepts discussed in the chapter. The key is the idea that it really is not too healthy to just live to eat. You can go by that principle during your set meal times, but outside of meals, it would be better to find other hobbies or things to do in order to occupy your time.

4. Keep our metabolic health under control

Action Steps

1. Use Medicine 3.0 to help monitor your ALT, sugar, cortisol, and other levels.

2. Examine the components of the foods you eat.

3. Ask yourself if you consume too much sugar and fats, and adjust your menus to suit your body better.

4. Check your family for their health histories.

5. Again, have yourself regularly checked, especially if you have worrisome symptoms such as inflammation, gut-weight gain, obesity, and the like

Checklist

1. Invest in a weighing scale for your meals

2. Look for recipes that are low in sugars and fats

3. Exercise to help prevent high ALT levels and lose visceral fat

4. Ponder on what you might be able to do for yourself if you are having what is considered a bad habit of eating at the moment. (essentially eating throughout the day with no period of rest for the body). If you are addicted

to food for some reason or the other, try to come up with ways with which you are able to at least control part of the addiction. A way could be to couple what you like (eating foods you like) with what you ought to do (exercising). That way, you only eat when you deem that you have exercised sufficiently.

Ch 7: The Ticker: Confronting – and Preventing – Heart Disease, the Deadliest Killer on the Planet

Summary

The last chapter looked at liver disease and metabolic dysfunction. At this point, we know that not only alcohol can destroy our liver. Problems with our metabolism can contribute to the accumulation of fats which can create a fat pile up in our liver. It's not even only a matter of who's obese or not. Some thin people develop NAFLD because their bodies have problems processing fats and sugars. Genes and lifestyles could have contributed to this susceptibility.

Developing heart disease is another way fat accumulation can shorten longevity. Fat is not just dangerous because of the weight gain it can produce but also because it can cause various cardiovascular diseases.

Drugs and other medical procedures and interventions that target the prevention of blood clots are great but they may not be enough. However, it is notable that they have contributed to our longevity, and that's at least something.

As diseases become deadlier than ever, Medicine 3.0 must continue to keep up. For example, atherosclerotic cardiovascular disease (ASCVD)is grave. Chances of dying from it are ten times higher as compared to that from breast cancer.

When Peter was only in his mid-thirties, doctors found high calcium levels in his coronary arteries. It sounds serious, right? Yes, it is, especially since such levels are generally more to be expected from someone 55 or older. It's a good thing that he decided early on to prevent heart disease from developing. It is at least a disease that can be prevented more easily than cancer orAlzheimer's. Early detection may feel devastating initially, but it's a way to save lives.

Apolipoprotein B is the main cause of atherosclerosis. The slow-moving disease can affect young people, too. So, even young people should start being careful with what they eat. After all, it is also when we are younger that we develop habits and preferences. It's just a reminder because some families let their younger members eat whatever they want just because they're still young. Starting good habits earlier is still the best preventative measure.

If you go through a CT angiogram and the doctors find a scar, it means your body was trying to create a barrier of protection. This damage can be calcified and will also show up in a calcium scan. So, yes, the damage was undoubtedly setting in, and it's time for you to act. Your body had tried to save you somehow.

Even though the scars are signs that your body is trying to protect you, you know that you are only a few more steps closer to feeling more cardiovascular damage. The plaque can become unstable or rupture or erode, causing the formation of clots.

You may have already heard about how clots can be scary. Well, they are. They narrow your arteries, thus blocking your lumen. It's what causes a heart attack or even a stroke.

To monitor your status with regard to the risk of developing ASCVD, you need to do Apo B tests, especially if you're genetically or physically more at risk of developing heart disease. However, even if you appear healthy, you should still make such tests mandatory. They can help detect a potentially life-threatening disease when it's just about to happen or is at an early stage. When you already have heart disease, you can no longer get back to a 100 percent perfectly functioning heart.

As for avoiding developing atherosclerosis, limiting or altogether avoiding it requires a low LDL-C level (low-density lipoprotein-cholesterol)

Lessons

1. With Medicine 3.0, prevention is the best way to tackle heart disease.

2. CT scans, calcium scans, and Apo B protein concentration tests can help detect the beginnings of cardiovascular disease.

3. ASCVD is many times deadlier than breast cancer and has been causing many deaths in the United States alone

4. ASCVD is one of the worse among Horsemen or slow death diseases. You can, however, prevent it by detecting it early and changing your lifestyle as a response to the diagnosis.

5. Even if one manages to live long, even with cardiovascular disease, the quality of life is poor.

Issues surrounding the subject matter

1. Do you have any family members with heart disease?

2. Do you have heart disease? If not, what are you doing to prevent it?

3. If you have a family history of heart disease, are you getting regularly checked by a cardiologist?

Goals

1. Understand just how deadly cardiovascular diseases can be and how they can prevent longevity.

2. Know that Medicine 3.0 is all about preventing and intervening early so that these diseases won't develop in the first place.

Action Steps

1. Understand how deadly cardiovascular disease is and how it can significantly shorten lifespan.

2. List the ways the chapter explains you can prevent serious cardiovascular diseases and how you can nip them in the bud.

3. Create a record of the steps you have been taking to prevent heart disease. If you already have a heart condition, what are some of the health moves that help you manage it?

Healthy Habit	Result/What it does for you

Checklist

1. Be aware of your family's cardiovascular health profile. Please find out how much of it is brought upon by genes, eating habits, lack of exercise, and other possible factors.

2. Find a cardiovascular disease specialist who can monitor you according to your current health.

3. Get checked for calcium levels and Apo B levels.

4. Improve your eating habits and preferences.

5. Regularly exercise. If you haven't exercised in a long while, you must be cleared by a physician first. Find a good trainer to help you with exercises that fit your health, age, and body type. Medicine 3.0, after all, is all about the individual.

Ch 8: The Runaway Cell: New Ways to Address the Killer That Is Cancer

There's no way we can discuss longevity and not touch on cancer. These days, cancer has wrecked a multitude of lives. Fortunately, advanced medicine has put cancer in remission for those who have caught the disease early.

Dr. Attia reminds us that it is difficult, if not impossible, to deal with cancer that is already at its latter stages. You need to use your immune system to deal with cancer. However, that's difficult when your body is already shutting down because the cancer is quite advanced. It's why you may hear of people who die so soon after their cancer diagnosis. They have gotten themselves checked too late.

Medicine 3.0 has so much to offer if you can get cancer detected early. After all, Medicine 2.0 found a way to battle leukemia.

It is no wonder that Peter's strategy against cancer is mostly about prevention. Working yourself into a state where you can no longer help yourself become healthier is not worth the risk. It's preferable not to get sick at all.

Here are the three parts of his strategy:

- Cancer avoidance
- Immunotherapy
- Cancer detection

The first part of the strategy is ideal as you follow practices that will help you avoid cancer as much as possible. It deals with health and nutrition practices.

Immunotherapy works when cancer is still in its early stages. It can be done when you already have the disease but the treatment can still be effective enough to get you better.

Cancer detection is done to check for the disease. At its early stages, cancer can still respond to interventions.

There is no single gene that causes cancer. There are a few factors that make it happen. Another promising tool that can help in fighting cancer is genome sequencing.

When dealing with cancer, it is essential to figure out what is causing it. Finding out what is causing it is also a way to amp up the prevention part of the strategy.

Here are possible factors contributing to cancer:

- Type 2 diabetes
- Smoking
- Obesity
- Metabolic dysfunction
- Insulin resistance

- Visceral fat

Watching your diet is undoubtedly essential. There are things that you shouldn't be taking too much of. For example, increasing insulin levels can contribute to cancer development.

An insulin-minimizing ketogenic diet is an ideal starting point for preventing cancer. Most of us know what foods are good for us, which ones we need to limit our intake, and which we shouldn't eat.

With dietary interventions, chemotherapy also works better. CAR-T is effective in targeting tumors and treating B-cell lymphoma. Meanwhile, adoptive cell therapy (ACT) seems to have a broader scope but is more expensive. It also takes much work to get ACT done compared to CAR-T.

Currently, reliable cancer screening tests are still limited to some parts of the body or cancer types. You can have them screen for lung, breast, colorectal, cervical, and prostate cancers. Still, it's a start that hopefully gains momentum toward other types of cancers.

You have the 4K blood test to test prostate cancer's aggressiveness. Blood tests should be combined with MRI imaging to create a better and bigger picture of what to expect and what should be done.

Colonoscopy is used to detect colorectal cancer; low-dose CT scans can detect cancer cells growing in our internal organs.

Lessons

1. Dr. Attia's strategy focuses on preventing cancer. He knows that if the disease is allowed to advance, it will be harder to cure.

2. A sound immune system is vital in battling cancer. So, if you're already at the later stages, your chances of getting better are slimmer.

3. Immunotherapy and cancer detection can also be done. However, again, they are better conducted during cancer's early stages.

4. In preventing cancer, it is essential to know what factors contribute to it so that you know what to avoid.

5. The Medicine 3.0 era presents several tests that can detect cancer. Still, they do not have a reliable test for every kind of cancer yet.

Issues surrounding the subject matter

1. Do you have family members who have been diagnosed with cancer?

2. Do you have cancer survivors in the family? What about those who have succumbed to their disease? Were they diagnosed early?

3. What were the first few symptoms if you have cancer in the family?

4. Are you concerned about any particular symptom you're experiencing?

Goals

1. To understand that even though cancer is a deadly Horseman disease, Medicine 3.0 has made way for some preventative measures and interventions.

2. Interventions are still better than cures. So, live a healthy life avoiding the factors contributing to cancer development.

3. To discover your cancer risks

Action Steps

1. Study your risks.

2. Live healthy to prevent cancers.

3. Be more aware of recurring symptoms that may suggest something as serious as cancer.

4. Begin a diary of symptoms. The symptoms may be nothing, but you can use the dates when you get checked by a physician. Your doctor can study your combination of symptoms and asks for further tests.

5. Think of ways which emotional health can be kept positive for the cancer patient. You may need a combination of a few factors to do that effectively. Knowledge about the disease as well as treatments will have to form the base, while knowing the patient's emotional inclinations will play into the next step.

Checklist

1. Again, check your family tree and health history for any cancers.

2. Keep a journal of symptoms to gauge if you have anything that may suggest cancer.

3. Get tested for cancers that are prevalent in our family

4. Live a healthy life by avoiding the factors that cause cancer

5. Check your insulin levels

6. Aggressive and regular cancer screening must be done to detect it early enough for you to eradicate cancer cells from your body.

7. Be careful to avoid being paranoid about cancer symptoms and signs; while you want to be aggressive in screening for it, do not think that every sign is a linkage to cancer.

Ch 9: Chasing Memory: Understanding Alzheimer's Disease and Other Neurodegenerative Diseases

Summary

Yes, people are scared to die and afraid to live a life they can't control. There's a loss of self-control when you start forgetting things.

With Alzheimer's disease (AD), much more can happen than losing memory. You may feel like the person is losing their identity, as well. That's a scary thing to happen, and we don't want it to happen to us. Alzheimer's can continue to get worse, to the point that we forget not just who we are but also some of the functions we take for granted. It's like becoming toddlers or babies again, helpless and needing other people's support. What's scarier is that you may not even know who the closest people to you are anymore. Alzheimer's is a neurodegenerative disease and arguably the scariest of the Horsemen diseases. It's one thing to be constantly in pain when you have cancer or a heart attack away from death, but slowly losing yourself while you're still alive is really scary.

Of course, understanding what it is about may help us better face and cope with its possibility. Some of the markers of Alzheimer's include Apo B concentration, LP(a) level, and APOE e4 allele gene. Alzheimer's is not reversible. Once you have it, that's it. Other neurodegenerative diseases we may want to avoid include Parkinson's disease (PD) and Lewy body dementia. They both affect movement and cognition.

Other less common forms of neurodegenerative diseases include Huntington's and ALS. Be wary, as these diseases can be dangerous.

A previous chapter has already mentioned that the e4 variant of the APOE gene suggests more tendency to develop Alzheimer's. Testing for the levels of this gene can help predict if a person will more likely have AD.

You may be on the lookout for some AD symptoms, such as:

- Cognitive impairment
- Depression
- irrationality
- Irritability
- Memory lapses
- Mood changes

Amyloid-beta, found in the brain's plaques, has been recognized as a contributor to AD. It can trigger brain shrinkage and inflammation.

So, really, the treatment and prevention of AD should focus on getting rid of or decreasing Amyloid-beta. Still, drugs that attempt to do this aren't successful yet. It would have helped in reversing AD if there were any success stories in using medicine to lower Amyloid beta levels.

However, the advantage of studying this disease is its vital genetic component. A person with AD will likely pass it on to his children.

While reversing AD isn't quite there yet, some practices can help maintain and improve cognitive function. Lifestyle changes that include eating well, exercising, and cognitive training help.

AD is said to be twice as common in females and is particularly risky to Caucasian, Hispanic, and Asian people. Meanwhile, Parkinson's disease is more likely to spread in women rapidly but is more common in men than women. Lewy body dementia is about the same.

Although there wasn't as much research material available for PD, it was still discovered that the genes SNCA and LRRK2 increase its risk. Some of the symptoms you will see in a person in the early stages of PD are:

- Handwriting changes
- Frozen face
- Changes in movement patterns
- Mild tremors

- Stooped posture

Lewy body dementia also displays the same symptoms as above, but a few additional ones:

- Anxiety
- Cognitive changes
- Depression
- Mood swings. It's almost like it put some of AD and PD's symptoms together.

To diagnose PD, a battery of tests should be conducted by a professional neurologist. It has also been found that exercise is the only way to delay its progression. The person must not give up, even with a devastating diagnosis.

With dementia patients, restoring blood flow through the brain can help prevent its progression.

Again, you can see a pattern here. There's much talk about delaying progression. Preventative practices and your immune system can help each other. However, they may not work well when you're already at the latter stages.

As for AD, studying metabolic processes can provide more prevention and cures for this disease. Detailed study and research are needed to help find more solutions to these neurodegenerative diseases.

At the moment, you can follow these health practices that are said to help prevent neurodegenerative diseases or at least delay their progression:

- Mediterranean-style DHA-rich diet
- Ketogenic therapies
- Endurance strength
- Grip strength exercises
- Treating depression
- Brushing and flossing teeth
- Vitamin D supplements
- Dry saunas

In short, treat your body as it's supposed to be treated but don't forget to be tested because some neurodegenerative diseases have vital genetic components.

Lessons

1. Neurodegenerative diseases can be some of the scariest diseases that significantly affect your quality of life.

2. Some people have a genetic predisposition to develop AD. So, studies have much material to work on. However, it's not good news for those with family members who have it.

3. Behavioral changes, forgetfulness, and tremors in movements are some of the common neurodegenerative symptoms you must look for.

4. Like any other disease, it is good to use preventative measures before the disease occurs or if it's still at an early stage. There is likely no reversal, but progress can be delayed.

5. Some health practices can help delay the progression of neurodegenerative diseases.

6. Getting monitored for the diseases can help you prevent or delay the onset of neurodegenerative disease.

Issues Surrounding the Subject Matter

1. Do you have family members with Alzheimer's or any other neurodegenerative diseases?

2. Have you been checked for the possibility of developing a neurodegenerative disease?

3. Do you have any concerning symptoms, including memory lapses?

Goals

1. Understand why neurodegenerative diseases happen.

2. Realize these diseases are more likely irreversible, but progress can be delayed.

3. Constantly check for the factors contributing to the increase in the chances of developing a neurodegenerative disease.

Action Steps

1. Add a section on neurodegenerative diseases to your journal of longevity and well-being.

2. Conscientiously fill the journal with all observations and tests.

3. Your health diary should already have a list of symptoms at this point. Go back to each one and write neurodegenerative, cardiovascular, liver disease, or any other disease you feel the symptoms may correspond to.

Example:

Symptom	Possible Corresponding Disease

Checklist

1. Get regularly tested for various neurodegenerative diseases, especially those in your family.

2. Keep your mind alert/go through cognitive exercises

3. Follow a regular exercise regimen

PART THREE

Ch 10: Thinking Tactically: Building a Framework of Principles That Work for You

Summary

In Part 2, we've looked at some possible diseases we can develop through our genes, habits, or environments. Even as Medicine 3.0 shows us some improvement in our healthcare, the risks of contracting such diseases have risen.

So, Chapter 10 tells us that we need to think tactically. It reminds us to build a framework of principles that will work for us. After all, Medicine 3.0 is all about catering to the individual's health.

Our environment keeps on changing. With it, our longevity continues to be tested. Again, you may say that people live longer lives now, but length is not equal to quality. You may be living a long life, but if it's not something you are happy about, then it's not how it's supposed to be lived.

You can't control some things, but there are those you can. So, you should focus on the five tactical domains that Medicine 3.0 wants you to look at:

- Exercise
- Diet (nutritional biochemistry)
- Sleep
- Emotional health
- Exogenous molecules (drugs, hormones, molecules)

The above are tactics that everyone should employ in their lives. However, it is the implementation that matters. How you implement it will differ from how somebody else will. It's because Medicine 3.0 takes into consideration the individual.

This chapter aims to have you assemble all you know and use the tactics you see fit for your health and lifestyle.

Based on your data, you can use the different tactics how you think they should be used in your life. Then, you check the effects of those tactics on your health. It means you are constantly adjusting until you find the right lifestyle. It should be something doable - something you can maintain.

Think about it. If you use a so-called miracle diet, will you be able to continue to upkeep the low-calorie intake advised for you? More likely, you won't be able to sustain the practice. Instead, you'll end up slowing down your metabolism.

Once your metabolism is slower than it was before, you'll have a more challenging time losing weight and getting rid of fat from your body. So, you may end up being worse off than when you started.

Among the tactical components, nutrition and exercise are the most complex. Of course, we still must coordinate them with the other tactics to make things work well.

It is also worth noting that your aim is not to lose weight but to lose fat. You can check your tactics by getting triglycerides and liver function tests. They will tell you more than weight loss or gain would be able to.

Tactics can be combined with trial and error as you try to find the best way to monitor, maintain, and improve your health.

Here are some tests that you may need to keep your data updated.

- Oral glucose tolerance tests
- Body composition data
- Bone density

The above are just some of the data you need to know where you are regarding your health.

Lessons

1. You need to follow reliable tactics to ensure you are in your best health or at least help prevent Horsemen diseases from developing.

2. Your holistic health is essential. None of the tactical points should be taken for granted.

3. Finding a holistic health regimen involves a lot of trial and error.

4. Your personal health data, environment, and lifestyle will feed the tactics you need to use.

5. Medicine 3.0 requires you to work on your individual self. Your tactic may differ from someone else even if it gets close enough to someone with the same family history.

Issues Surrounding the Subject Matter

1. Have you applied any or all of the health tactics to your life?

2. Have you had your glucose levels, body composition, and bone density assessed?

3. What do you think are the obstacles for yourself if you aren't implementing any or all of the health tactics mentioned?

4. What do you think could be other health tactics not mentioned here that may be effective for yourself?

Goals

1. Create our own set of tactics to fight dangerous diseases

2. Understand the importance of having a custom set of tactics

3. Accept the fact that nutrition and exercise are the most complex among the tactical domains

Action Steps

1. Embark on a trial-and-error but consistent and persistent journey towards breaking terrible health habits and predicting dangerous diseases while at their earliest stage.

2. Create a suitable exercise regimen and diet according to dynamic biomarkers discovered after taking crucial tests.

3. Ponder on how you can also help to strengthen the portion on emotional well-being. This particular segment can have a deep impact on your holistic health and thus should receive quite a bit of attention from you. Have you been neglecting your emotional health? What should you do if you find yourself having done so? Can you think of any wholesome activities which you can do to give yourself a boost in positivity?

Checklist

1. Analyze the results of various health tests

2. Examine your family history

3. Study the five tactical domains and find out how you can excel in each, with a greater focus on exercise and nutrition.

4. Based on the previous steps, create your own set of tactics.

5. Take steps to ensure that you can create a good sleeping habit, and also to be able to have a good sleeping environment.

Ch 11: Exercise: The Most Powerful Longevity Drug

Summary

As the previous chapter states, exercise is one of the most complex tactical domains. Chapter 11 confirms it. In fact, not only does it say it is powerful in terms of its impact, but it also says that it is, in fact, the most complex. However, it is imperative to understand it because it affects our longevity.

We need to engage in aerobic fitness and high-strength exercises specially designed for our health, age, and body type to increase our lifespan and health span. Again, here, we must be reminded of the importance of customizing our health regimen to who we are and at what point we are in our health journey.

If your body is aerobically fit, you can harness more energy. With more energy, you can do more of the things you love to do. When you do that, you are happier. Your longevity is then associated not just with the actual longer life span but also with good quality.

Peak cardiorespiratory fitness is measured by V02 max level (the rate which a person can utilize oxygen). So, those with higher VO2 max levels are expected to live longer. When someone is fit, he can create more ATP (the fuel for our cells) by taking in more oxygen.

Regular training can help a person make the most of exercise. It will then increase VO2 max levels. Strength and muscle mass, as we already know, contribute to a person's capacity to exert force.

A lot of severe diseases and conditions can be avoided when someone exercises regularly:

- Pre-diabetes
- Diabetes
- Heart diseases
- Stroke

Why? It's because exercise strengthens our circulatory system. It improves our mitochondrial health and enhances metabolism. We already know what happens when our metabolism goes haywire.

So, just by exercising, we solve and prevent several potential problems simultaneously. Remember Dr. Attia talked about how a metabolic disorder can cause various serious diseases? Well, exercise has been one of the solutions recommended to prevent or delay their progression.

As you grow older, you will lose some muscle. However, exercise can also counteract the natural effects of aging. You can keep your muscles firm if you regularly exercise. You may need strength training and aerobic exercises combined to keep fit through the years.

Peter suggests that exercise be considered a prehab. It's like physical therapy, and it helps maintain a robust musculoskeletal structure. Dr Attia lays special emphasis on what the Centenarian Decathlon is all about. It consists primarily of a list of physical tasks, like hiking up a hill or having sex, which would be the objective of folks when they hit 90 or even a 100. It is about getting rid of the stereotype that older people are weak and that mindful exercise can contribute to a better quality of life.

Lessons

1. Exercise is the most complex tactical domain in longevity.

2. Those who exercise regularly can attain higher levels of VO2 max.

3. People with higher levels of VO2 max are more likely to live longer and less likely to get seriously sick.

4. Exercise should have an aerobic and strength component.

5. Exercise can keep you strong and healthy and keep your muscles firm even as you age.

Issues Surrounding the Subject Matter

1. Do you reserve some time for regular exercise?

2. How much time can you spare for exercise per session or per day?

3. Do you exercise at a gym, outdoors, or inside your house?

4. Do you have a trainer?

5. Have you had yourself checked by a physician before choosing an exercise regimen?

6. If you haven't been exercising, what are your plans regarding exercise?

7. What alternatives can you think of in place of exercise if you choose not to actively pursue exercise?

Goals

1. Understand that exercise is the most complex and one of the most critical health tactical domains.

2. Create an appropriate and customized exercise regimen for yourself.

3. Target good health and long life by actively seeking exercise.

4. Know what to check for when testing for physical fitness.

Action Steps

1. Get yourself checked by a physician to see just how fit you are.

2. Have a professional design an exercise regimen, especially for you

3. For the folks who have not been exercising and are finding it tough to start for some reason, think of some positive effects you wish to see due to exercise. List them out and make them part of your motivation package to start putting in the physical work.

4. Always remember, there is always a certain amount of exercise that is suitable across all ages and across all levels of fitness. Find the right fit for yourself and remember not to over do it.

Checklist

1. Examine your current exercise regimen, if existent.

2. Analyze your health status.

3. List your most relevant health concerns.

4. Check your health journal for your data.

5. Have a professional look at your current or lack of exercise regimen and see what can be done to improve it based on your current health status.

6. Regularly exercise.

7. Record your exercise instances in your health journal (date, duration, effect on you, etc.)

Ch 12: Training 101: How to Prepare for the Centenarian Decathlon

Summary

Dr. Attia mentions a Centenarian Decathlon earlier. Right now, just the thought of that happening makes you slightly worried for the ones involved. After all, some 40 or 50-somethings may already be complaining of all kinds of ailment.

The Centenarian Decathlon is not really what it seems. You can prepare for it in any stage of life, whether you're in your early twenties or in your late sixties.

When preparing, you cross check your exercise regimen, with the intention to use it for longevity.

Yes, the primary purpose is longevity. It's not just about weight loss or looking great in our swimsuits, although those are great bonuses. Still, it's all about living a higher quality life for longer.

So, your exercises should include cardio, strength, and stability.

We hear about cardio a lot. As its name suggests, it promotes cardiovascular health. It also strengthens our lungs. It's all about endurance while training to reach higher VO2 max levels.

Strength is all about building muscle and being able to avoid injuries successfully. Meanwhile, you should be able to apply stability to your cardio and strength exercises.

Our metabolic health depends on the utilization of fatty acids and glucose. These components shouldn't be left in large amounts in our bodies.

You need to maintain healthy mitochondria with the help of a healthy metabolism and strong athletic performance. The mitochondria should remain healthy because it is in charge of whether fat accumulates in our bodies or not.

The first stage of preparing for the Centenarian Decathlon is efficiency training and aerobic endurance. This stage is vital for mitochondrial health.

As we age, the quality and quantity of mitochondria decrease. However, mitochondrial biogenesis can reverse or delay that. Zone 2 exercises are those which you need to perform at the beginning of your Centenarian Decathlon preparation.

Here are some examples:

- Cycling
- Rowing
- Running

- Walking
- Elliptical training

These exercises can improve cerebral blood flow, cognition, and any other conditions that can affect whether you develop a neurodegenerative disease such as Alzheimer's or not.

As for other aspects of our health, Zone 2 exercises may be suitable for your cognitive ability, but they can only increase VO2 max levels by a little. Still, it's all about priorities and mixing and matching. Remember that the whole journey toward longevity is full of trials and errors.

To maximize your VO2 max training, you must do at least five to six months of zone 2 work. Again, these numbers can change based on your health. You must get regularly checked for health markers that matter the most with your current health status.

Of course, it shouldn't be a one-time thing. The VO2 max training should continue for years. As much as you can, you should continue doing it. It is suitable for your longevity. It doesn't matter how old you are. The more you take on these exercises, the higher your VO2 max levels will be. You can keep on improving yourself.

Another concern about getting old is the decrease in muscle mass and strength. Your muscles will also weaken as you age. However, Zone 2 exercises can at least delay the progression. That's how crucial exercise can be to your longevity and quality of life. Zone 2 endurance exercises can protect you from atrophy in muscle 1 fibers. On the other hand, atrophy in muscle 2 fibers can only be corrected if you use significant resistance.

As mentioned in the previous chapter, you can use DEXA to measure bone density. It can also be used to measure body fat and lean mass. Low bone mineral density (BMD) is commonly associated with taking too many corticosteroids, estrogen-blocking drugs, smoking, malnourishment, and low muscle mass. It also has a genetic factor.

Dr Attia also reminds us of something that seems commonsensical and yet taken for granted: what we can carry with our hands depends on our strength. It involves hip-hinging movements, grip strength, and pulling motions.

Peter recommends that we perform the farmer's exercise to prepare for the Centenarian's Decathlon. It will help us with grip strength. As for eccentric strength, we need some pull-up and pull-down exercises.

Before performing the suggested exercises above, you should check your stability through strength and movement tests.

Lessons

1. To help us achieve longevity, we should perform exercises as if preparing for a Centenarian Decathlon.

2. Fitness has three dimensions: cardio, strength, and stability.

3. Zone 2 exercises help us improve our aerobic efficiency.

4. Our health needs to improve our VO2 max levels.

5. We should test and train ourselves for grip strength, pulling movements, hip-hinging, and concentric and eccentric loading to improve our strength.

Issues Surrounding the Subject Matter

1. How would you describe your current strength and endurance?

2. How is your balance?

3. Can you run a significant distance without feeling winded?

4. Does having an exercise partner help you achieve your goals?

5. What are your VO2 max levels like?

Goals

1. Create an exercise regimen that addresses cardio, strength, and stability.

2. Train as if working towards a Centenarian Decathlon, otherwise known as improving our longevity.

3. Work on Zone 2 endurance exercises before moving on to VO2 max-level exercises.

4. Create a regimen that can be sustained for years.

5. Work on strength exercises like a farmer preparing to carry heavy loads.

6. Check for BMD and VO2 max levels.

Action Steps

1. To understand that preparing for a Centenarian Decathlon is all about preparing our bodies for the long haul

2. To address all facets of a good exercise regimen

3. To test for and analyze your current strength, cardiovascular health, and bone density

4. Analyze your health readiness.

5. List your current health strengths and weaknesses in the first rectangle.

6. List your target health characteristics that will help you reach a hundred years old in the second rectangle.

1st Rectangle

2nd Rectangle

Checklist

1. Get checked for BMD, VO2 max levels, and overall cardiovascular health

2. Have a physician give you the clearance to perform specific exercises

3. Work with a trainer who can provide you with a guide to exercises you can perform and sustain through the years

4. Back up your exercise regimen with good nutrition

Ch 13: The Gospel of Stability: Relearning How to Move to Prevent Injury

Summary

The previous chapter focuses on cardio, strength, and the overall potential exercise has on keeping us alive for longer and in good health. Chapter 13 looks at another vital facet of exercise, stability.

Without stability, you may be unable to complete your exercises without incurring an injury. It would help if you had stability so that you could perform your regimen with safety and ease.

When approaching exercise, we must consider how to do it safely. It's why trainers will tell you to warm up first. Even your physical education teacher made it clear when you were still at school. You can't just jump into more complex moves. You need to prepare your body. You also need to stabilize your body.

An injury, take note, does not only affect your body. It can also have a severe psychological impact. You've probably heard of people fearing returning to a particular activity after a hard fall that may have caused a fracture or a similarly devastating injury. It's best to avoid it. It can still happen even if you are prepared, but at least you can reduce the instances and impact. Athletes who are excellent physical specimens also sometimes have injuries, but that's because they take more significant risks.

Peter believes that stability is the foundation of fitness and strength. It helps the body to spread energy to parts of the body where it's needed. So, not only should you be strong, but you should also be flexible, agile, and fluid.

It is better to begin stability exercises at a young age. When we get older, we will lose much of what we may have gained when we were young. We are more likely to be more ungainly and clumsier.

So, you must go through stability training with DNS (dynamic neuromuscular stabilization) and other fundamental stability principles in mind. Breathing exercises may also assist in the whole regimen.

Before you begin, you should go through respiration and movement tests. These tests will help you better understand where you are. Based on your status, you will be provided with a suitable respiration strategy.

Breathing is a great way to jump-start your stability. It starts with stabilizing your mind and also affects your physical state.

While we instinctively know that breathing affects relaxation, we should know that it also helps balance us physically.

Three types of breathing exercises are hyper-inflated, compressed, and uncontrolled. Breathing exercises also help with your body position, such as:

- Neck position
- Spine shape
- Rib position
- Feet position

In DNS training, you learn intra-abdominal pressure (IAP), which helps activate our true core. It's good to note that IAP is a foundation of stability.

People who do hyper-inflated breathing should do their stability training with weights. Meanwhile, those who do compressed breathing should work with cross-body rotation exercises. Finally, those that work with uncontrolled breathing will have to do a lot of closed-chain exercises, including push-ups.

The feet are a more prominent source of stability. After all, they take all the weight of our body when we are in an upright position. When they have balance, they can protect the rest of the body, especially the hips, knees, ankles, and spine.

One of the initial stability tests is to stand on one foot. You need to be able to keep the stance for at least 10 seconds.

When training strength, you must ensure your spine is safe and protected. Studies show that the cervical spine often has the most degeneration or wear and tear.

If you do yoga or at least have heard of some exercises, you should be familiar with the cat or cow pose. When you are performing and holding these poses, you can better understand the segment control levels in your bodies.

With stability, we can safely pass on energy and power from one point of our bodies to another. We transmit the energy to our muscles and bones to perform some activities safely.

Most of the things above may be common knowledge. Another thing to note here would be the shoulders, which are the most vulnerable because they have several different muscular attachments.

Now, let us take a look at our hands. We also need stability in our hands. If someone can successfully modulate and transmit force through their hands, they can effectively do push and pull movements.

We can continue to zero in and look at the fingers. Bicep curls can help with finger strength.

One way of knowing if you're progressing is to record videos of your exercise sessions. That's the only way you can see yourself in action. You may try to work out in front of mirrors, but that means working in a gym or dance studio. It also means studying your movements when you are still doing them.

With video copies of what you did, you can check your progress after the fact. You can see the difference between what you are trying to do and where you still are regarding your physical health progress.

Now, let's go back to the Centenarian Decathlon. After all, you are doing everything to ensure you live a long, healthy, and happy life. Barry Get Up is a simple regimen that you can work with.

What is "Barry Get UP?" It's basically getting up using one arm or no arm at all. The latter is the better version for testing stability. You can try to fit this into your daily life and see how it works out for you.

Lessons

1. Before exercising for longevity, you should check your stability first.

2. Stability helps you keep your balance so that you can avoid injuries.

3. Stability is the foundation of fitness and strength.

4. You start exercising for stability through breathing exercises.

5. There are three types of breathing: hyper-inflated, compressed, and uncontrolled.

6. The feet are essential factors in keeping your balance and stability.

7. Breathing exercises help with the following: neck position, spine shape, rib position, and feet position.

8. You must safely pass energy and power from one part of your body to another.

Issues Surrounding the Subject Matter

1. What exercises have you been doing regularly?

2. On a scale of 1 to 5, how fit are you?

3. How balanced are you?

4. Do you do breathing exercises for physical health and/or emotional health?

Goals

1. To begin with, stabilize yourself before you exercise.

2. Find some breathing exercises that can help prepare your body for exercise. Deep breathing in and out may be a good primer for starters as it brings in the oxygen to charge up your body.

3. Keep yourself safe by doing warm-up exercises first.

4. Use your stability to keep yourself from injury while moving forward to some exercises that can help your body achieve good form and the ability to hone your body for longevity.

5. Stability helps maintain fluidity, agility, strength, and flexibility.

Action Steps

1. Understand why stability is the key to fitness, strength, and longevity

2. Work on simple stability exercises before doing other type

(See Table on next Page)

Exercise Log – Date:			
Exercise	Type (cardio/strength/stability)	Reps	Weight added (if applicable)

Checklist

1. Warm up before exercising

2. Go through stability exercises

3. Have someone spot you or record you are doing your exercises

4. Watch your videos to see what your stability is like

Ch 14: Nutrition 3.0, You Say Potato, I say Nutritional Biochemistry

Summary

In this chapter, Peter talks about how we don't fully understand what various diets do to our bodies. Every diet that comes out touts itself as the best one. However, there's often no conclusive proof.

Dr. Attia himself used to follow the ketogenic diet. He said that it had helped him correct his metabolic syndrome. In the end, even though that worked for him for a while, no diet works for everyone the same way. You may think of it as a confirmation of Medicine3.0's focus on the individual, or you may also think of it as a matter of nutritional biochemistry.

Even nutritional biochemistry may not give you the holistic answer you need. It only deals with the science of food and nutrition. It does not address the emotion, ideology, and religion you may depend on when picking your desired food.

Considering everything you want and need, you can say your goal is to follow Nutrition 3.0. Nutrition 3.0 puts together feedback and data with science. So, you end up with something that fits you.

Why?

Think about it. Everyone has different nutritional needs. Some people are undernourished, while others are over nourished. Some have poorly developed muscles; at the other end of the spectrum, you'll find some overly muscular ones. Generally, you may consider decreasing your energy intake and working towards lean mass.

So, the first thing to do is look at your current nutritional needs and overall health. Then, you can use proper eating patterns and nutritional intervention according to your needs. Restoring your metabolic equilibrium decreases the chances of developing severe chronic diseases.

What should you be looking out for when you look at proper nutrition?

- Adequate calories for your bodily processes and activity level
- Essential fats
- Sufficient proteins for maintaining muscle mass
- Essential vitamins and minerals

Of course, you may also ensure you don't take in harmful toxins. Junk food, too much fat, and too much salt and/or sugar are just some things you shouldn't be adding to your diet as much as possible. Some people can handle them even less than others because of predispositions to cardiovascular diseases, diabetes, and other chronic diseases.

Clinical trial studies and epidemiology decide what is good for us to eat. Some foods are generally good or bad, although each person's actual ratio may differ. These factors represent the scientific parts of your diet.

However, it would be best to consider many other factors that complicate choosing the proper diet.

- Educational level
- Genetics
- Income
- Religion
- Metabolism
- Advertising

Some people may not have the educational level required to know what foods are unsuitable. Some may not have the income to buy healthier options and may have to make do with cheaper junk food.

Religion may also affect your dietary choices. Many religions present healthy options. So, they're not going against the science. However, some religions take things to the extreme and prohibit foods needed to keep you in tip-top shape.

As Nutrition 3.0 will emphasize, we are all different. Metabolism can be different in each person. That's another thing that should be considered when choosing your diet.

Then, there's advertising. Sometimes, we are just attracted to images we are constantly bombarded with. The foods that are continually being advertised are not always healthy, either.

Clinical trials are more insightful than epidemiology but can't give you the complete picture.

Ultimately, looking at your nutritional intervention regarding efficacy versus efficiency would be best.

Efficacy deals with the intervention's performance when you follow the rules and operate under perfect conditions.

Meanwhile, efficiency deals with the intervention's performance under real-world conditions.

Lessons

1. Remember that nutrition, aside from exercise, is one of the most complex tactical domains when working towards longevity.

2. Even if a diet is effective for you as an individual, it doesn't mean it's as good for others.

3. Nutrition 3.0 follows on the heels of Medicine 3.0. it operates on everyone's individuality.

4. While our bodies generally require the same essential elements, they may each need a different ratio.

5. Science will provide us with a specific diet that everyone can understand as a good thing. Still, real-world examples make things a lot more complicated.

Issues Surrounding the Subject Matter

1. What are your daily activities like?

2. How many calories do you need daily based on your physical activity, age, height, current weight, and health?

3. Does your religion prohibit you from eating certain foods?

4. Do you have any health conditions that prohibit you from eating certain foods?

Goals

1. Understand that while there are diets that will generally work for most people, they don't cater to everyone.

2. Understand that you need to eat well for good metabolism and longevity

3. Know your nutritional needs.

4. Find a diet that will work for you based on science, epidemiology, and other real-world factors.

Action Steps

1. Know if you need nutritional intervention.

2. Find the diet that works for you in terms of all the factors that matter to you.

3. Use nutritional biochemistry to decide what kind of diet is right for you

4. We shouldn't focus on just one diet everyone's been promoting (e.g., keto, paleo, etc.)

5. Choose foods that will help us maintain good metabolism.

6. Take the useable from the different diets and put them to use for yourself. Different diets may have certain positives which can then utilized to create a personalized diet plan that is quite suited to your personal needs. For example, the ketogenic diet

expounds low carb high good fats, while the mediterranean diet goes for green vegetables and rich polyphenols found in fruits as well as vegetables. You can delve deeper into each diet and adopt the aspects which may be more suited to you.

Checklist

1. Get checked by a physician to see if you are over nourished, malnourished, or just right.

2. List the foods you are allergic to, if applicable.

3. List the foods that your religion or other ideologies prohibit you from eating.

4. Based on what is available for you, create a diet that will maintain your health if you don't need an intervention or improve your health if you do need an intervention.

Ch 15: Putting Nutritional Biochemistry into Practice: How to Find the Right Eating Pattern for You

Summary

This chapter continues on the previous topic of nutritional biochemistry. The previous segment focuses on the mistakes that we have made when deciding on our diets. It also tackles the difficulty of adding real-world conditions when making choices.

This time, we will be looking at the correct pattern for you. This is in line with following Nutrition 3.0.

Unfortunately, foods that cause more harm than nourishment are being promoted everywhere. They are advertised to look delicious, and they are! However, indulging in them can cause us to succumb to some of the Horsemen diseases, which are the prime enemies of longevity. Let's take a look at the Standard American Diet. We may joke about it, but we can see that it's been pushing junk food on us. These meals totally go against the nutritional goals we should be pursuing. This diet destroys our metabolism, making us store more fat than our bodies need and raising glucose levels that our bodies are not equipped to handle.

Now, let's go back to the previous chapter's rule. We shouldn't rely on one particular diet plan. In this chapter, we are made to see exactly why that is the case. A typical popular diet plan relies on one or more of the following strategies:

- Restricting calorie intake (CR)
- Restricting diet (DR)
- Time restriction (TR)

Thus, restriction seems to be the name of the game. CR or calorie intake restriction can only work well in a perfect environment. You must follow the rules to a tee, and your metabolism must work well to handle the sudden loss of calories. Also, there aren't a lot of reliable tracking tools for CR. Imagine giving up most of your time to sit down and calculate every little thing that goes in your mouth. It can become an unhealthy, obsessive practice.

DR is pretty popular at this point. Some people think they'll be fine if they avoid certain foods. Here's the thing, however. Again, we are all different, with varying metabolism. A diet should contain all the macronutrients required by the body. So, if you follow DR, you may deny your body some nutrients it needs. Here, the difficulty is sitting down and choosing the foods your body shouldn't take in.

Then, there's the currently trending strategy, TR. What is it exactly? It's otherwise called fasting. This strategy should only be taken in extreme cases.

Now, let's go back to some basics. We know that carbohydrates are the primary energy source. It would help if you had it in some form. So, you can't just avoid all carbohydrates. However, you may need continuous glucose monitoring (CGM). It helps understand your carbohydrate tolerance and how your body responds to them.

Your diet and nutrition may have to be modified according to your CGM result. Based on that information, you may or may not need significant lifestyle changes. While deciding on your diet, other factors, such as age, sex, exercise habits, and more, may have to be considered.

CGM is not the only thing that you can do. Other biomarkers need to be monitored, such as the following:

- Body composition
- Fat mass
- Insulin
- Lean mass ratio
- Liver enzymes
- Lipids
- Uric acids

We need proteins and amino acids to maintain and build lean muscle mass. It provides our body's structure, the building blocks. Even if you don't need them for energy, you must ensure you keep your muscle mass.

Every day, you need 1.6 grams per kilogram minimum protein intake. Peter mentioned it in a previous chapter, and he mentions it again. DEXA can be used to measure muscle mass. He recommends taking in at least 4 grams of lysine and leucine daily.

Protein intake not only helps us with our muscle mass on its own, but it also helps us with our metabolism. Taking in protein helps us feel satiated. If that messes up, we will find ourselves looking for more food to fill us up.

With fat, it's a different thing. It can act as both a source of energy and as building blocks for our cells. However, taking in too much fat will mess up your metabolism. Still, it has its role. Ingesting the right amounts of the right kinds of fat helps in stabilizing your metabolism and in keeping your brain healthy.

There are three types of fats:

- Saturated fatty acids (SFA)
- Mono-unsaturated fatty acids (MUFA)
- Polyunsaturated fatty acids (PUFA)

There are two kinds of PUFA: Omega 6 and Omega 3. Omega3's subdivision includes EPA and DHA.

Fatty foods have all three types. So, it's impossible to take one and skip the others. Peter believes we should have 50 to 55% MUFA and 5 to 20% SFA levels. The rest will be reserved for PUFA.

Medicine 3.0 and Nutrition 3.0 remind you that different individuals react to fats differently. So, it's all about finding the right mix for you while monitoring the various biomarkers mentioned earlier.

Ultimately, your overall health, age, gender, biomarker levels, and activity levels will decide whether you should go for DR, CR, TR, or some intricate combination of all three.

Again CR can work in a perfect world, where you can count your calories without it taking over your life. Combining it with exercise can help you achieve better results.

As for DR, you need to take note of the information mentioned about carbohydrates, proteins, and fats and how, ideally, our bodies still need a portion of all of them to achieve a balanced diet.

Then, we have TR, which should only be an emergency tactic.

Lessons

1. There are three main types of restriction diets: calorie, diet, and time restriction.

2. It is not wise to depend solely on one type of popular diet.

3. Monitoring specific biomarkers will help you find the correct diet pattern for you.

4. Your body still needs carbohydrates, proteins, and fats. Still, you must understand that Nutrition 3.0 reminds us that our bodies react differently to them.

5. The Standard American Diet (SAD) should be avoided as much as possible as it generally pushes us to eat junk food.

Issues Surrounding the Subject Matter

1. Why do you think fasting should be used only as a last resort? Or do you have alternative views with regards to this?

2. Have you tried calorie restriction before and how did it go for you? More importantly, was it sustainable for any meaningful length of time?

3. What are you thoughts on the Standard American Diet? How much of it can you trust and what do you think about needing to find out information for yourself?

Goals

1. Find out where your metabolism level is at

2. Find the most appropriate restriction diet type for you

3. See if combining CR, DR, and TR is the best solution for you

4. Understand that everyone reacts to different diets differently

5. Understand your risk profile

6. Find a nutritional intervention or appropriate diet pattern that you can adapt for the long haul (sustainable)

7. Understand that nutrition is only a part of the overall picture. There's no need to overthink the whole thing, or your stance on food may become obsessive.

Action Steps

1. Be vigilant about what you are eating

2. Know what is in the food that you eat

3. Check ingredients and nutritional information when buying foods from groceries.

4. Avoid processed foods as much as possible.

5. Monitor your biomarkers before, during, and after you've chosen the proper diet for you.

<u>Example of a Food Diary Entry below</u>

Food Diary – Date:	
Food	Ingredients

Checklist

1. Check your biomarkers and see where they stand

2. See if there are some foods you shouldn't take much of, depending on your current health levels, and take them from your lists.

3. Use a weighing scale for your meals as much as possible without being consumed by the practice.

Ch 16: The Awakening: How to Learn to Love Sleep, the Best Medicine for Your Brain

Summary

This chapter reminds us that the combination of good quality and optimal quantity of sleep is beneficial for our brain. You need to sleep well in order to:

- Improve your memory
- Maintain your emotional equilibrium
- Sustain your cognitive function

So, not sleeping well can threaten your memory and state of mind. State of mind here refers to your ability to learn and understand facts and process your emotions.

If you don't sleep well, you won't get a chance to clean your brain. You will feel muddled and packed with stressful thoughts and emotions. When sleep doesn't feel as refreshing as it should be, you should get your sleeping patterns and quality tracked. Based on the results, you can be provided with an action plan.

What are some of the things that affect the way we sleep? Here are some:

- Artificial lighting
- Emotions
- Noise
- Stress
- Sunlight

Ideal sleep should be within the 7.5 hours to 8.5 hours range. Good quality sleep is compared to a performance-enhancing drug.

A lot of us underestimate what sleep can do for us. After all, there are so many things that need to be done. We can develop insulin resistance and poor metabolism when we don't sleep well. So, it's not just tiredness you'd get when you do not get that proper rest from the bedroom.

Not sleeping well can trap you in a vicious cycle. It will make you stressed, and your stress will, in turn come back to prevent you from sleeping well.

Sleep deprivation can also lead to high cortisol and high overnight glucose reading. You may also find yourself eating for comfort more.

There are even worse complications when you don't sleep well. For example, your risk for dementia and Alzheimer's increases.

Great sleep consists of the complete three stages:

- Non-REM (light)
- Non-REM (deep)
- REM (rapid eye movement)

REM sleep provides emotional awareness, while non-REM deep sleep provides emotional healing. It's like going through therapy, from acceptance to healing, in one night if you sleep right.

When you sleep deeply, your brain disposes of waste that shouldn't remain and could weigh down on you emotionally.

So, if you know you have a sleeping disorder, you should accept it. This way, you can move on to the next step – finding a solution. The solution can be as simple as changing your sleep hygiene or using sleep trackers. Still, you may need medication for conditions such as sleep apnea. The STOP-BANG testing can check for this disorder.

Other tests that can check for various sleeping disorders include the Insomnia Severity Index, Epworth Sleepiness Scale, and the Pittsburgh Sleep Quality Index.

To help you sleep, you can prepare the following sleeping environments:

- Keep lighting at a minimum, if there's lighting at all

- Turn off screens early and keep them off the sleeping area as much as possible
- Keep the room at a 65 F or any cool temperature that is comfortable for you
- A warm bath before bed to relax you
- Zone 2 exercises to help generate adenosine (for sleep pressure) can be done about two to three hours before bed.
- Meditation for relaxation

Night owls may need a little more help. Those with severe insomnia may benefit from cognitive behavioral therapy (CBT).

Lessons

1. Every stage of sleep is essential in nourishing us mentally, physically, and emotionally.

2. Not sleeping well can affect your state of mind and how you interact with people and your environment.

3. Great sleep consists of three stages

4. It would be best if you had a good sleeping environment to sleep well

5. When you sleep well and deeply, your brain disposes of waste – the stress and the emotional turmoil that you were in when you were awake

Issues Surrounding the Subject Matter

1. How many hours, on average, do you sleep?

2. Do you have a sleep ritual?

3. What is your sleeping environment like?

4. What are the last couple of hours before sleep like?

5. Do you feel refreshed in the mornings?

6. Do you have a hard time falling or staying asleep?

7. Have you been diagnosed with sleep apnea?

8. Do you find yourself dealing with work or playing with mobile/pc games right up until the time you get to bed? Would you consider this overdigitalization? Would you like to perhaps go for a digital detox then?

Goals

1. To understand the importance of sleep

2. To know which types of sleep are necessary for mental and emotional health

3. To prepare proper sleep hygiene or environment that will help you reach your 7.5 to 8.5 hours

4. Find ways to relax your mind so that you can sleep more quickly and better

5. Go for holistic health by going through exercises that can help both your mind and body

Action Steps

1. Prepare a sleep journal just like the one below:

Date	How long it took you to sleep	Sleeping aids/rituals	How long you slept (to fill in the following day)

2. Analyze your entries and work toward improving your sleep quality based on what you see there.

3. Going into a deep state of meditation can help to prepare your mind and body to get rest better. If you find that you are one of the folks who are kept on the laptop or phone all the way until bed time, then you may want to do this: slot out perhaps 15 minutes or half an hour before actually going to bed and use that allotted time to meditate. The most important thing you should focus on during this time would be to get your mind to calm down. You can mentally chant mantras in your mind " may I be well and happy " until you find your mind being able to concentrate on just a singular object. Then you can switch focus to your in and out breath.

Checklist

1. Prepare a journal of your sleeping habits that you can fill in regularly.

2. Get checked for sleeping conditions.

3. Work on exercises and other rituals to help you get tired enough to sleep to avoid insomnia.

4. Learn relaxation techniques that will help ease your mind for better mental health, which can contribute to better sleep.

Ch 17: Work in Progress: The High Price of Ignoring Your Emotional Health

Summary

Throughout this book, Dr. Attia clarifies that physical health is affected by emotional health. He reminds us that we may have to pay a high price if we focus only on our physical well-being. We need to keep our mental state and emotions healthy, too.

Peter uses drug addiction as an example. Being an addict affects not only your body but also your mental and emotional health.

An addict displays the following behaviors:

- Anger
- Detachment
- Insecurity
- Obsessiveness

These are behaviors that Dr. Attia has personally dealt with and is willing to talk about. He believes in being able to unpack our pasts and deal with them.

Peter advises that we find tools to help us function better emotionally. He talks about how therapy played a part in getting him to deal with past traumas.

The trauma tree network and equine therapy are a couple of things that therapists can use to help alleviate the considerable produced by trauma. This past pain that continues to linger can be referred to as either a small T or big T trauma.

Peter reminds us that adversity and trauma are different from each other. He says that children are built resilient against the latter. However, there are times when trauma can be so significant, or the sufferer is unequipped to deal with it that he grows up to become a troubled or troublesome adult. Trauma leads to dysfunction when the person suffering does not have the tools to cope with it. It's not recommended to make comparisons either. Everyone's different. Everyone has a different trauma and a different way of coping with it. One pill can't solve everyone's problems.

It is essential to figure out that there's something wrong with us emotionally. This way, we can remedy the situation quickly.

Here are some of the things that we can do to keep ourselves mentally and emotionally well:

- Going on vacation
- Spending time with the family
- Relaxing with a hobby
- Meditate daily for at least 30 minutes in one sitting

Different people may have different ways of taking a break mentally or emotionally. Do what makes you feel a lot better.

When working on ourselves emotionally, we should also learn how to look within ourselves and see our actions from the point of view of others. Doing this allows us to work out what we are doing wrong and see other people's struggles.

Peter discusses a combination of treatments, medication, stabilizers, and self-exploration. One of the points he keeps returning to is understanding ourselves and our relationships with ourselves. He also recommends dialectical behavior therapy and mindfulness medication.

As for interventions, breathing exercises are recommended. Slow and deep breathing can be great additions to weekly therapy sessions. Therapy may also be needed so that someone can help you with your journey to understand your pain better. Someone who isn't too close to the situation can objectively help you see what's wrong with it. So, even if you think you can self-examine, you must still consider getting outside help.

One of the most significant problems we have is recognizing the problem. We need to identify our problem first before we can admit it and do something to resolve it. It is also crucial that we know we can seek help. After all, aren't we trying to outlive because we have people we care about that we want to live for? We can also let them help us become better.

Lessons

1. Your emotional and mental health is just as important as your physical health.

2. Someone with emotional problems may become an addict or display the symptoms of addiction.

3. Trauma is different from adversity.

4. Different people deal with trauma differently.

5. Admitting that something is wrong with us is the first step toward improving.

Issues Surrounding the Subject Matter

1. What is your overall physical health like?

2. How about your emotional health?

3. Which are you taking care of better: physical or emotional health?

4. Is there a chance you are taking care of yourself holistically?

5. Do you have any childhood traumas that continue to bother you today?

6. How do you cope with your trauma?

7. How is it different from the adversity that you face as an adult?

Goals

1. Identify any past traumas that you still need to get over.

2. Understand how these traumas are affecting your life today.

3. Clear your mental fog and your emotional and mental issues.

4. Face your traumas and fears and find a sustainable solution.

5. Understand that you need to have overall good health because longevity is not only about living longer but also about living a good life.

Action Steps

1. Analyze yourself.

2. Seek the help of a therapist to identify any past traumas that still weigh you down today.

3. Write your thoughts about past traumatic situations in your diary.

4. Use physical exercises that improve not only your physical health but also your mental health.

5. Consult your therapist on some of the best physical exercises to help you overcome the traumas you are still suffering from.

Example of an exercise that helps ease tension and alleviate symptoms of trauma:

- Stand with your feet flat on the floor.
- Make sure you feel comfortable with your chosen stance.
- Your feet should be shoulder-width apart.
- Lean to one side, pressing your weight in that direction.
- Use the outer edge of your foot on the side you are leaning toward. Get some help from the inner side of the other foot.
- Breathe deeply and slowly two to three times.
- Lean towards your other side, fixing your feet position accordingly.
- Repeat the leaning on each side two to three times.
- Stretch.

Checklist

1. Examine your life, especially your behaviors and issues.

2. Trace your behaviors back to an incident or situation in your childhood that may have prompted them.

3. Seek the help of a therapist if you are having difficulty identifying the issue or getting over your trauma.

4. Keep yourself healthy physically and mentally.

Conclusion

Dr. Peter Attia has clarified that longevity may not be how we initially see it. It's not just a matter of reaching the age of eighty, ninety, or one hundred. Instead, it's about reaching those ages while enjoying a healthy and happy life.

The author confesses that for a time, he subscribed to the Silicon Valley way of hacking human biology's for longevity. These people continue to look for the best gadgets and diets that can turn humans into "perfect little humanoids," as Attia refers to them.

However, Attia realizes soon enough that longevity doesn't matter if your "life sucks."

Some people live a long life supported by all sorts of medication. Some may even have to go through a lot of medical procedures just to survive. It's better if we can prevent that from ever happening by keeping ourselves healthy.

Mental health is also important. You may live a long life, but it's nothing if you're constantly living in sadness and dysfunction. It's time to face your past traumas and see what you can do about them so that you can live the rest of your life with fewer worries.

Hopefully, you'll be able to use the knowledge and recommended activities in this workbook to help you achieve longevity in its true form. Again, longevity is about living a long, satisfying life. So, keep yourself healthy. Cover all the five tactics. Get some health management ideas from your physician and therapist if needed.

May you be well and happy